REST IN PEACE
RASHAWN

WRITTEN BY: RONNIE SIDNEY, II, MSW
ILLUSTRATED BY : TRACI VAN WAGONER

Rest in Peace RaShawn

Published by Creative Medicine: Healing Through Words, PO Box 2749, Tappahannock, VA, 22560

Library of Congress Control Number: 2017901390
ISBN 978-0-9986011-2-0 (Hardback)
ISBN: 978-978-099-000-8 (Paperback)
ISBN 978-0-9986011-1-3 (Paperback)
ISBN 978-0-9986011-3-7 (eBook)

PRINTED IN THE USA

Rest in Peace RaShawn
Written by: Ronnie Sidney, II, MSW
Illustrated by: Traci Van Wagoner
Designed by: Kurt Keller
Edited by: Tiffany Carey Day, Francesca Lynn and Samantha Willis
Contributor: Lawrence Jones

Please visit www.nelsonbeatstheodds.com for information about "Rest in Peace RaShawn", "Nelson Beats the Odds", "Tameka's New Dress", and "Nelson Beats the Odds Compendium One". The "Nelson Beats the Odds Comic Creator" app, teacher's guide and mixtape are also available on the website. Follow us on social media and use the hashtag #RipRashawn #TamekasNewDress, #NelsonBeatsTheOdds, #NBTO and #iBeatTheOdds.

 @nelsonbeatstheo

 @nelsonbeatstheo   @ronniesidneyii

 Nelson Beats The Odds
Ronnie Sidney, II, MSW
#iBeatTheOdds

 @nelsonbeatstheo   @ronniesidneyii

Creative Medicine: Healing Through Words, LLC

FOREWORD

Our young people are being traumatized daily by directly experiencing violence, or viewing violent videos of men, women, and children being killed by private citizens or police officers. My hope is that "Rest in Peace RaShawn" gives young people a platform to process police-involved shootings, gangs, and grief. As adults, it's essential that we're physically and emotionally available to help our young people through these processes.

Over the summer I met with a diverse group of young men at a Virginia academy to talk about my book series. The event was in the wake of the officer-involved shootings in St. Paul, Baton Rouge, and Dallas. I deviated from my initial presentation because I knew the recent shootings were on everyone's minds. I divided the young men into groups of six and asked them to answer the following questions: What solutions do you think will bridge the divide between communities of color and the criminal justice system? What are your opinions on the recent officer-involved shootings? What is it like to be Black or Hispanic today? The questions and answers give a real voice to a fictional story, and are presented throughout "Rest in Peace RaShawn".

First Print 2017

"Airsoft guns are replica firearms that shoot plastic pellets (also known as BBs) by way of compressed gas or electric and/or spring-driven pistons. Depending on the mechanism propelling the pellet, an airsoft gun can be operated manually or cycled by either compressed gas such as Green Gas (propane and silicone mix) or CO2, or by compressed air via a spring or an electric motor pulling a piston. All these products are designed to be non-lethal and to provide realistic replicas." (Nediyi, 2012)

"What is it like to be Black or Hispanic today?"

 "Bad, frightening, upsetting, frustrating, and fearful for our lives."

HABIB, A LOCAL STORE OWNER, WATCHES JEREMY WAVE HIS AIRSOFT GUN AND CALLS 911.

RASHAWN GOES TO GET NELSON AND JEREMY FROM THE PARK BEFORE THE STREET LIGHTS CUT ON.

JEREMY ANXIOUSLY PUTS THE AIRSOFT GUN UNDERNEATH HIS HOODIE.

Q "What solutions do you think will bridge the divide between communities of color and the criminal justice system?"

A "Analyze the situation better."

A POLICE CAR AGGRESSIVELY PULLS UP ON THE CURB AND JEREMY TAKES OFF RUNNING.

OFFICER MARTINEZ CATCHES UP WITH JEREMY AND TACKLES HIM FROM BEHIND.

I DIDN'T DO ANYTHING. GET OFF OF ME. I CAN'T BREATHE!

"What are your opinions on the recent officer-involved shootings?"

 "We don't really feel safe around officers and that burns many bridges with them. We don't trust most of them. Are they really out to protect and serve or to annihilate and conquer?"

OFFICER JACOBS SHOOTS RASHAWN FIVE TIMES. JEREMY SCREAMS...

OFFICER JACOBS APPROACHES RASHAWN WITH HIS GUN DRAWN.

HE SHOT ME. ALL I WANTED TO DO WAS SHOW HIM IT WASN'T REAL...

HE PICKS UP THE GUN, SEES THE ORANGE TIP, AND REALIZES IT WAS A REPLICA.

"What is it like to be Black or Hispanic today?"

"I am 6'5", 255 pounds... It's scary for me, I feel like I have to do all I can to make others not fear me. So, that's why I'm always telling you guys, look, hey, scoot off to the side of the street, or make way for other people. I'm always thinking, how can I not make that other person feel like I'm a threat."

Q "What is it like to be Black or Hispanic today?"

A "We feel sad because people are being shot for no reason."

"What are your opinions on the recent officer-involved shootings?"

"It's sad, but it's not really unexpected because police have been killing Black people for so long, so now, nobody can be surprised that people are starting to get mad and resist."

"What solutions do you think will bridge the divide between communities of color and the criminal justice system?"

 "Here in America, if you're for one thing, then it's perceived that you're against the other. Nowadays, if you're pro-Back Lives Matter, then you're anti-cop. If you're pro-cop, then you're anti-Black Lives Matter. We need to look for a solution where someone can be pro-cop and pro-Black Lives Matter."

THE NEXT NIGHT, JEREMY SITS OUTSIDE ON THE STOOP TO CLEAR HIS MIND.

LIL' G AND MEMBERS OF THE SAUCE STREET GANG APPROACH HIM.

WHAT'S UP LIL' HOMIE?

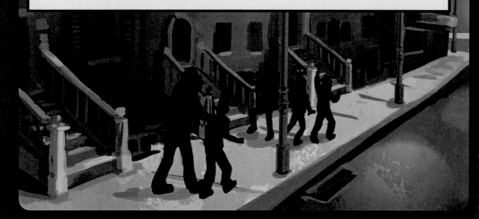

JEREMY JOINS LIL' G AND HEADS TO HABIB'S STORE.

AFTER JEREMY SPRAY PAINTS HABIB'S STORE, LIL' G HANDS HIM A BANDANNA AND INITIATES HIM INTO THE SAUCE STREET GANG.

AS THEY WALK AWAY, THE STORE GOES UP IN FLAMES.

CHURCH, MY HEART IS HEAVY THIS AFTERNOON. RASHAWN WASHINGTON WAS ONE OF OUR BEST AND BRIGHTEST MEMBERS OF THIS COMMUNITY. I REMEMBER WHEN HE WAS STRUGGLING WITH A MATH CLASS IN THE FIFTH GRADE. I TOLD RASHAWN THAT FOR EVERY "A" HE GETS ON HIS REPORT CARD, I'D GIVE HIM $10. RASHAWN WOULD COME UP TO ME AFTER CHURCH EVERY NINE WEEKS WITH HIS REPORT CARD. HE WOULD GREET ME WITH THIS ENORMOUS SMILE AND SAY, "TIME TO PAY UP, OLD MAN".

TO SISTER MARY, PUT YOUR FAITH IN THE LORD. YOU LOST A SON BUT GOD HAS GAINED ANOTHER ANGEL. RASHAWN LOVED YOU AND HIS BROTHER MORE THAN LIFE ITSELF. TO JEREMY, RASHAWN WOULD WANT YOU TO KNOW THAT IT WASN'T YOUR FAULT. YOUR BROTHER UNEXPECTEDLY BECAME PREY TO A FATE THAT HE TRIED SO DESPERATELY TO PROTECT YOU FROM.

CHURCH, LET'S NOT LET RASHAWN'S DEATH BE IN VAIN. WE MUST NOT REST UNTIL JUSTICE IS SERVED.

"What solutions do you think will bridge the divide between communities of color and the criminal justice system?"

"It's going to take a lot of communication and hearing from both parties on how we can communicate and come to a conclusion that works for everybody, so that everybody feels safe."

"It's a cold world. Where is the love and peace? It seems like life is on repeat. Dude had a toy gun and they still shot him. It seems like what Dr. King fought for doesn't even matter, they still want to see our blood splattered. It seems like if we talk, we get a bullet. It makes me think about what to do in life. Do I need to carry a gun? I go to church and they say something about what they are going to do, but I don't really see them doing anything. People talk a big game about how they are going to stop racism, but when it's time for action, no one is around. Police or people in general assume what other people are going to do with a gun, thinking they're right and we're wrong. The movie Fruitvale Station comes to mind. In the movie, the black dude (Michael B. Jordan who plays Oscar Grant) didn't do anything and got shot. For what reason? If you want something done you have to take a stand and fight. Maybe not physically, but mentally like Dr. King. He fought with words, Rosa sat. There is a difference in fighting for what you believe in and fighting with violence. People make mistakes but don't want to be corrected. It makes me think, are we really free or free to think we're free. We all have two ears, two eyes, one mouth, one nose and red blood. Why are we doing all of this because of color? We are different shades of light. Some lighter, some darker. Black is just a darker shade of light. We all have one brain, we are all bright. Take a stand."

Lawrence Jones, 16, Portsmouth, Virginia

ACKNOWLEDGEMENTS

This project would not have been possible without the grace and mercy of the Most High.

To my fiancé Talisha, and daughters Mali and Morgan, thank you for your patience, love and understanding.

To Imagine That! Design, thank you for bringing my stories to life and providing quality service. Special thanks to my editors and contributors, Tiffany Carey Day, Lawrence Jones, Francesca Lyn, and Samantha Willis. I'd like to give an extra special thanks to my junior editorial team, Dion Allen, Jamal Ball, Christian Brown, Diojé Ellis, Tiojé Ellis, Ricardo Henson, Terrell Hundley, Tamaje Jones, and Isaiah Taylor.

To my beautiful and supportive family: Ronnie Sidney, Sr., Gwendolyn Sidney, Cherlanda Sidney-Ross, Van Ross, Deandre Sidney, Sydney Ross, Endia Ross, Robert Patrick, Sarah Harris, Etta Wright, Gail Wright, Tony Harris and Gil Holmes.

To some very special individuals and organizations: MP-NNCSB; Chuck Walsh; Emily Eanes; Rachel Teagle; Richmond Association of Black Social Workers (RABSW); Kevin Holder; Renata Hedrington-Jones, PhD; Daryl Fraser; Virginia Commonwealth University (VCU); Nicki Lee, PhD; Mayor Levar Stoney; Understood.org; Virginia Department of Education; Anne Holton; Marianne Moore; Ellen Harrison; Pat Abrams, PhD; Martha Hicks; Essex County Public Schools; Ruth Tobey; Patrick Doyle; Virginia Education Association (VEA); Dr. Antoinette Rogers; Martha Hutzel, Central Rappahannock Regional Library; Meldon Jenkins-Jones, Richmond Public Library; Chris Brown; Karla Redditte (NBC 12); Towanda Darden (EYPC); Ernestine Scott (RPS); Erica Coleman (RPS); Dawn Owens; Alabama First Class Pre-K; Dr. Kimberly Johnson; Essex Public Library; I'm Determined; John McNaught; Kim Stump; Cayden Stump; JMU Male Academy for Academic Achievement Academy; De'Shay Turner; Clovia Lawrence; Julie Bright; Sean Miller; Deanna Lavery; Chad Lewis; Shawn Long; Christopher Pitts; Sean Powell; Derek Hence; Christopher O'Neal; Ebony Campbell; David Miller; Kwame Alexander; Margaret Ransone; Chris Rose (Rappahannock Times); Rich Morgan (WRAR); Kelsee Scott; Rappahannock Community College; Reynolds Community College; Old Dominion University; Good Hope Baptist Church.

To the rest of my family and friends, thank you for your support and words of encouragement throughout this difficult project.

In closing, I wish to dedicate this book to the memory of Michael Brown, William Chapman, Danroy Henry, Jr., Aiyana Jones, Trayvon Martin, Laquan McDonald, and

Made in the USA
San Bernardino, CA
08 April 2017